COLORING BOOK

15 DECADES
Women, Style & Innovation

From the Gilded Age to the Teensies

instagram: @jenracinecoloring

f

facebook.com/jenracinecoloring

www.jenracine.com

ABOUT THIS BOOK

This book contains facing pages for each decade with 15 decades in all — from 1870 to 2010. Each era is labeled with its most common nickname along with an illustration of a woman and hairstyle that is representative of the time. Other details include, the most popular name for a girl during that decade, common slang, and various beauty and household items. In most cases, a technological advance like a radio, typewriter or phone is included.

All of these items are believed to be accurate according to internet research from various sources (including wikipedia, libraries and museums). Every effort was made to make this book as error-free as possible, however, there may be some inaccuracies.

I hope you feel inspired by the women, style and history in this book.
Happy Coloring, Friends!

Tips for Coloring

This paper is best suited for colored pencil, gel pens or crayons. Markers have a tendency to bleed through. For all media, it's best to put one or several pieces of paper behind the page to prevent bleed-through and creasing on the next page.

———————

Find all JEN RACINE coloring books in online bookstores.

Find coloring pages on **Etsy:**
JenRacineColoring

THIN ICE

CHEAPSKATE

RAZZMATAZZ

CHEW
THE FAT

BRASS

1890'S

BATTLE
AX

1900's

Call on the carpet

Bash

In the bag

Humdinger

LAY OFF

EAT YOUR HEART OUT

JAZZ

GRIFTER

1910's

A GAS

ON THE MAKE

On the UP and UP

MALARKY

Rag-A MUFFIN

1920's

RITZY

CAT'S MEOW

Made in the USA
Columbia, SC
11 April 2023

15200875R00035